Note to parents, carers and teachers

Read it yourself is a series of modern stories, favourite characters and traditional tales written in a simple way for children who are learning to read. The books can be read independently or as part of a guided reading session.

Each book is carefully structured to include many high-frequency words vital for first reading. The sentences on each page are supported closely by pictures to help with understanding, and to offer lively details to talk about.

The books are graded into four levels that progressively introduce wider vocabulary and longer stories as a reader's ability and confidence grows.

Ideas for use

- Ask how your child would like to approach reading at this stage. Would he prefer to hear you read the story first, or would he like to read the story to you and see how he gets on?

- Help him to sound out any words he does not know.

- Developing readers can be concentrating so hard on the words that they sometimes don't fully grasp the meaning of what they're reading. Answering the puzzle questions on pages 46 and 47 will help with understanding.

For more information and advice on Read it yourself and book banding, visit **www.ladybird.com/readityourself**

Book
Band
9

Level 3 is ideal for children who are developing reading confidence and stamina, and who are eager to read longer stories with a wider vocabulary.

Special features:

Detailed pictures for added interest and discussion

Wider vocabulary, reinforced through repetition

We go to the toy shop.

In the shop, Lola says, "I can choose something VERY good here. I have to see it ALL first. I will be a VERY long time."

18

Longer sentences

Lola says, "Charlie, you are right. I will get this present for Lotta."

I say, "That is good, Lola. She will love it."

Simple story structure

30

31

Educational Consultant: Geraldine Taylor
Book Banding Consultant: Kate Ruttle

Text adapted by Jillian Powell
Text based on the script written by Carol Noble
Illustrations from the TV animation produced by Tiger Aspect Productions Limited

A catalogue record for this book is available from the British Library

First published by Ladybird Books Ltd MMXIII
80 Strand, London, WC2R ORL
A Penguin Company

This edition produced for The Book People Ltd MMXIV.

001

ISBN: 978-0-72329-373-6

Printed in China

You Won't Like This Present as Much as I Do!

Characters created by
Lauren Child

My name is Charlie.
I have this little sister, Lola.
She is small and very funny.

This is Lola. Her friend is called Lotta.

Lola also has an imaginary friend called Soren Lorensen.

One day, my little sister Lola says, "Charlie, I have some money to get my friend Lotta a really good birthday present."

"What will you get?" I say.

Lola says, "An actual real pony!"

I say, "But you don't have the money for a real pony. And Lotta's home is too small."

I say, "What about something useful to play with?"

Lola says, "A musical skipping rope would be good..."

"Hmmm," I say.

"What about wings, so Lotta can fly just like a butterfly?" Lola says.

But I say, "Lola, butterfly wings are not a real present! You must choose something real."

We go to the toy shop.

In the shop, Lola says, "I can choose something VERY good here. I have to see it ALL first. I will be a VERY long time."

Then Lola says, "Look, a doctor kit! I have always wanted one. And it is a useful toy because one day I may be a doctor in an actual hospital."

"But Lola," I say. "We are here to get Lotta a birthday present."

"But Charlie, I REALLY want this," says Lola. "I can get this for me and another present for Lotta."

I say, "But you will only have a little money left. Lotta's present will have to be very small."

"Lotta will REALLY love this very small ball," says Lola.

I say, "But you wanted to get Lotta something really good, not just a small ball."

"Lotta will not love the doctor kit as much as I do," says Lola.

I say, "Lotta will REALLY love the doctor kit, too."

"Hmmm…" says Lola.

Lola says, "I can actually see us playing doctors. I will say, 'Don't worry, all you ill people. I am a doctor. I can make you well.' Lotta will say, 'So can I!'"

Lola says, "Charlie, you are right. I will get this present for Lotta."

I say, "That is good, Lola. She will love it."

At home, Lola wants her imaginary friend Soren Lorensen to see Lotta's present.

"We can just unwrap it a little," Lola says.

Soren Lorensen says, "I don't think we should!"

Lola says, "Just one little look!"

"Well now it is ALL unwrapped, we could play with it," says Lola. "Soren Lorensen, you are ill at hospital but I can make you well because I am a doctor."

When I go in, I say, "Lola! You have unwrapped Lotta's present!"

Lola says, "It was an accident!"

I say, "It is not right to play with Lotta's present."

Lola says, "I could have it. Lotta may not like it."

"But it was for HER," I say.

Lola says, "You are right. Will you help me wrap it again?"

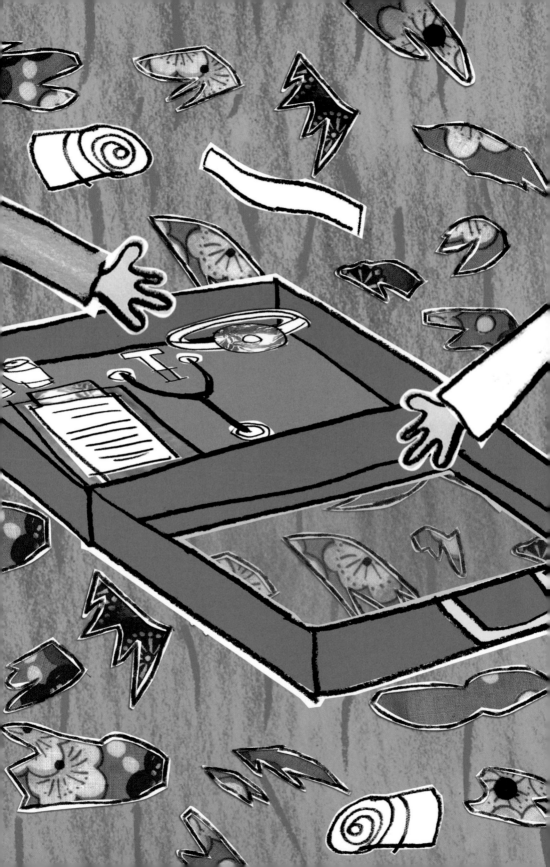

When we get to Lotta's house she says, "Lola! Is that present for me?"

"Yes, it is actually for you. Happy Birthday!" says Lola.

Lotta says, "A doctor kit! I REALLY wanted one! Thank you, Lola."

Lola says, "It has bandages AND a coat."

Lotta says, "I will put the coat on now."

"Look, we are actual doctors!" says Lola. "Doctor Lotta, is Charlie ill?"

Lotta says, "He has had an accident. He must have a bandage!"

I say, "What a good present!"

Lola says, "Yes. I choose presents very well!"

How much do you remember about the story of You Won't Like This Present as Much as I Do? Answer these questions and find out!

- Who is Lola going to buy a present for?

- What sort of shop do Charlie and Lola go to?

- Can you name two of the things Lola wants to get for Lotta?

- What present does Lola really want for herself?

- Who does Lola show Lotta's present to?

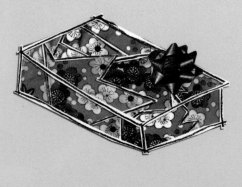

Look at the different story sentences and match them to the people who said them.

"Lola, butterfly wings are not a real present!"

"Lotta will REALLY love this very small ball."

"I don't think we should."

"Lola! Is that present for me?"

Read it yourself with Ladybird

Tick the books you've read!

YOU won't like this present as much as I DO!

The Elves and the Shoemaker

Hansel and Gretel

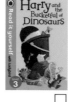
Harry and the Bucketful of Dinosaurs

Jack and the Beanstalk

Furi on Music Island

Poppet Stows Away

Rapunzel

The Red Knight